More MAKING THE GRADE · GRAD

EASY POPULAR PIECES FOR YOUNG PIANISTS. SELECTED AND ARRANGED BY LYNDA FRITH

Exclusive distributors:
Music Sales Limited
Newmarket Road, Bury St. Edmunds, Suffolk IP33 3YB.
This book © Copyright 1995 Chester Music
ISBN 0-7119-5050-4
Order No. CH61082
Cover design and typesetting by Pemberton & Whitefoord.
Printed in the United Kingdom by
Caligraving Limited, Thetford, Norfolk.

Chester Music

(A division of Music Sales Limited)
8/9 Frith Street, London W1V 5TZ.

INTRODUCTION

This collection of 16 popular tunes provides additional attractive teaching repertoire to complement the first books in MAKING THE GRADE. As with the previous books, the pieces have been carefully arranged and graded and the collection is made up of well-known material which pupils will enjoy. The standard of the pieces progresses to Associated Board Grade 1.

CONTENTS

ASLAN'S THEME

by Geoffrey Burgon

Memorise the last three bars of the right hand, paying particular attention to the movement of the thumb.

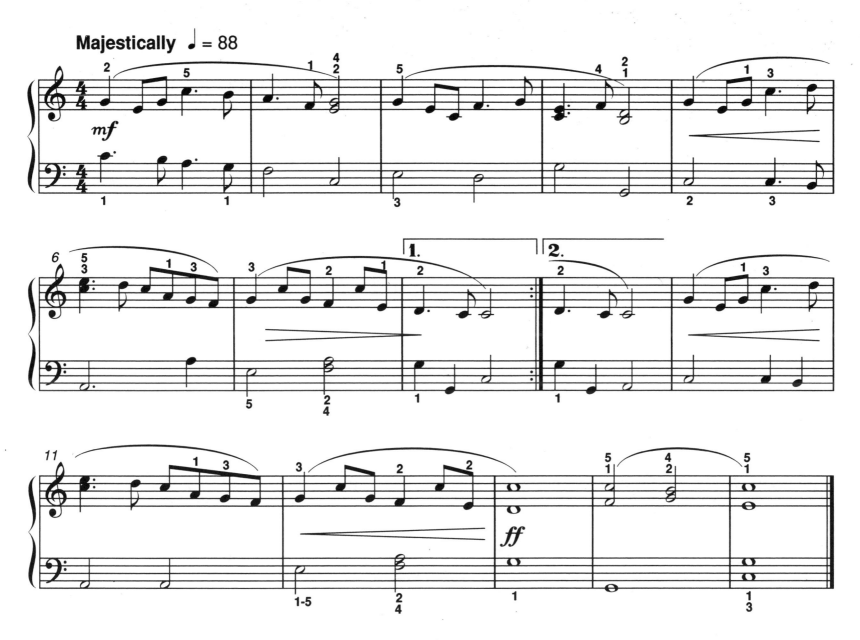

LOVE CHANGES EVERYTHING

by Andrew Lloyd Webber, Don Black & Charles Hart

Notice the phrasing in this piece, and try to make the music breathe as you play.

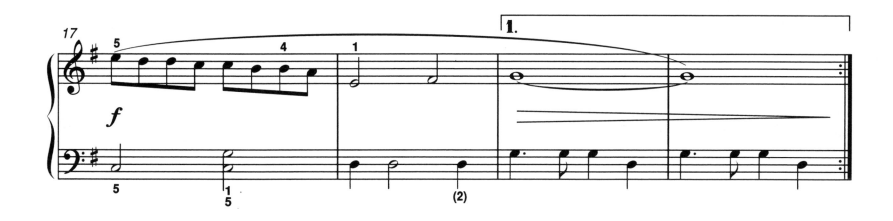

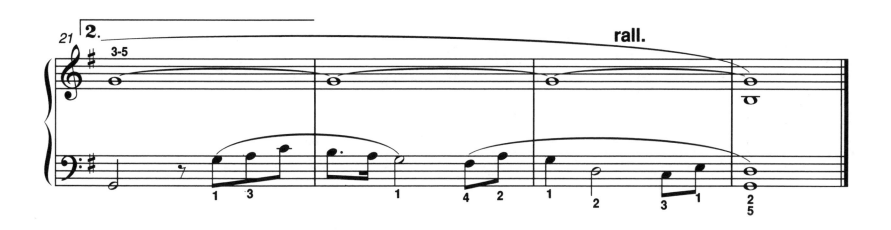

HAPPY XMAS (WAR IS OVER)

by John Lennon & Yoko Ono

The right hand and left hand each have their own tunes. For a change, try making the left hand louder from bar 25.

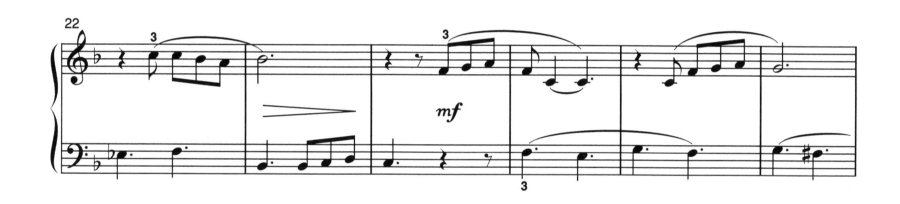

NELLIE THE ELEPHANT

by Peter Hart & Ralph Butler

At bar 25 the left hand takes over the tune from the right hand. Bring out the left hand at this point.

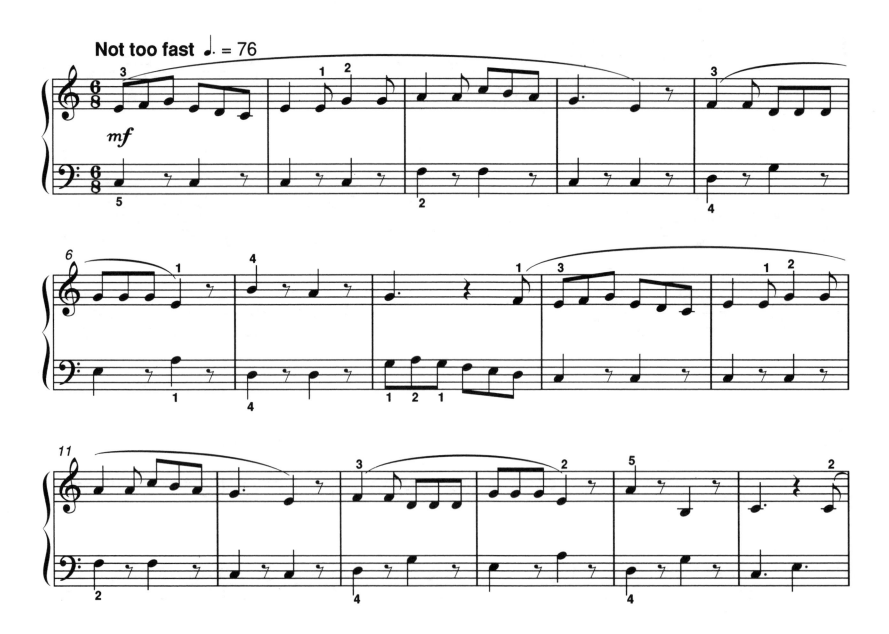

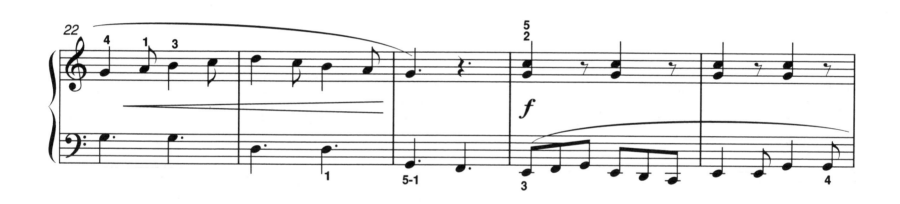

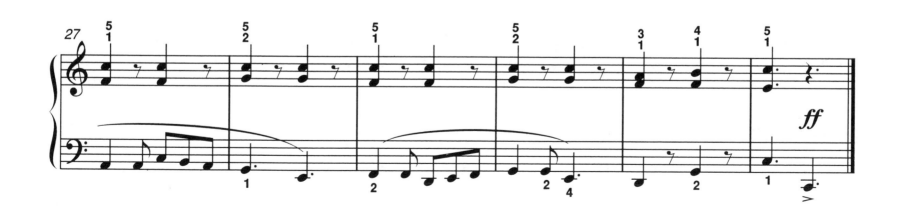

CASTLE ON A CLOUD

by Claude-Michel Schonberg & Herbert Kretzmer

The time signature changes every bar at the beginning and end of this piece, so be careful to keep a steady beat.

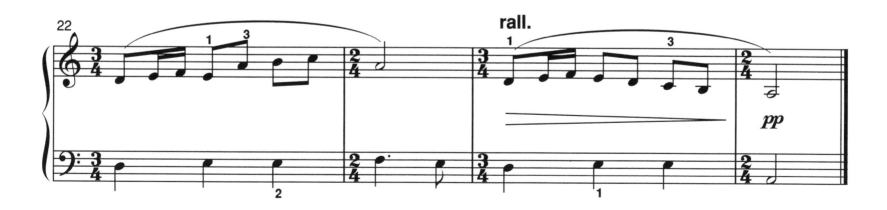

CATHY'S CLOWN

by Don & Phil Everly

Practise clapping the left hand syncopated rhythm in bar ten. Count aloud at the same time, stressing count three.

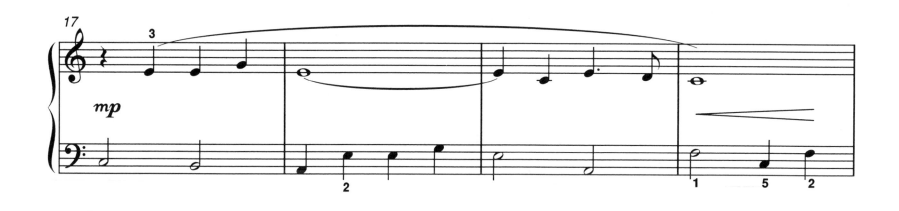

CLOSE EVERY DOOR

by Andrew Lloyd Webber & Tim Rice

This song from 'Joseph and the Amazing Technicolor Dreamcoat' is sung by Joseph when he is in Egypt.
Listen for the Egyptian-sounding phrase in the left hand, starting at bar eight.

LEAVING ON A JET PLANE

by John Denver

The syncopated rhythm ♩ ♫ ♩ ♩ occurs frequently. Make sure that you don't shorten the third beat.

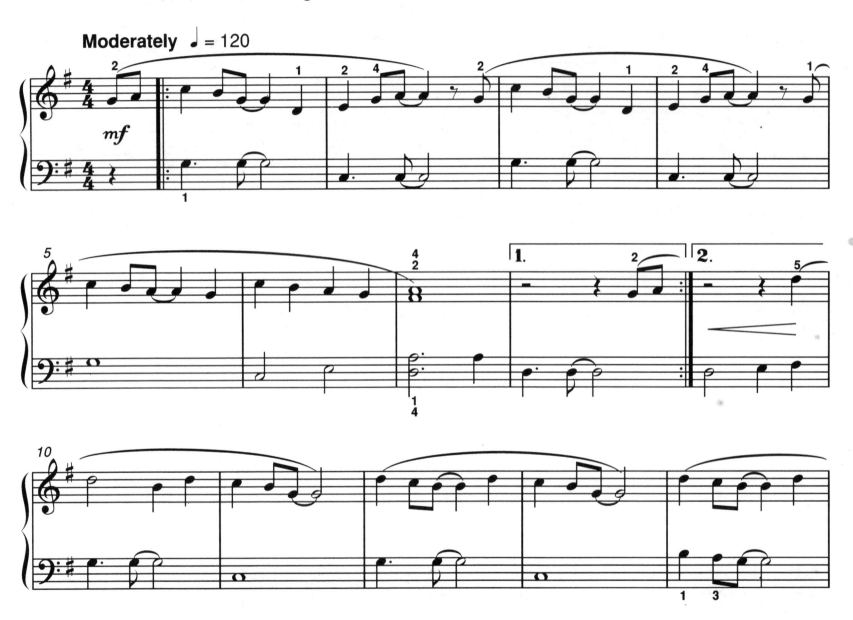

MUSIC OF THE NIGHT

by Andrew Lloyd Webber, Charles Hart & Richard Stilgoe

Try lifting your fingers before you play the right hand chords, and listen to check that the notes sound exactly together.

Slower again (♩ = 72)

19

HEY JUDE

by *John Lennon & Paul McCartney*

Look at the (♪♪♪ ♪♪) rhythm in bar five. Try tapping it first very slowly (♩ ♩ ♩ ♩ ♩) and gradually speed up. Accent the third note.

Fine

D.S. al Fine

KNOWING ME, KNOWING YOU

by Benny Andersson, Stig Andersson & Bjorn Ulvaeus

The final quavers of bar three are tied over into bar four.

Play the first left hand note of bar four strongly so that you don't lose the beat.

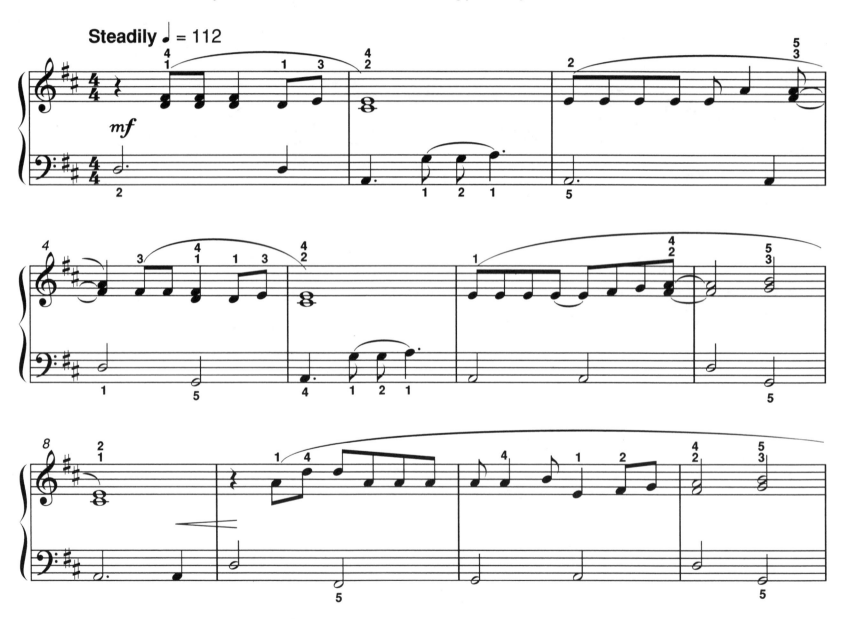

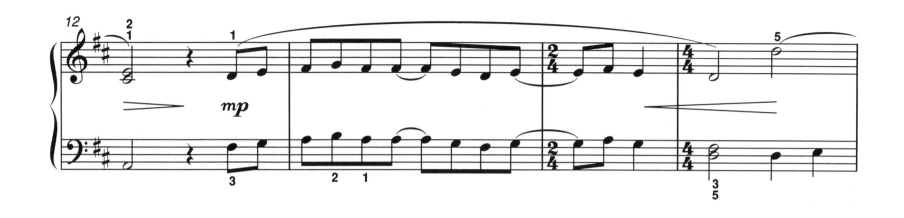

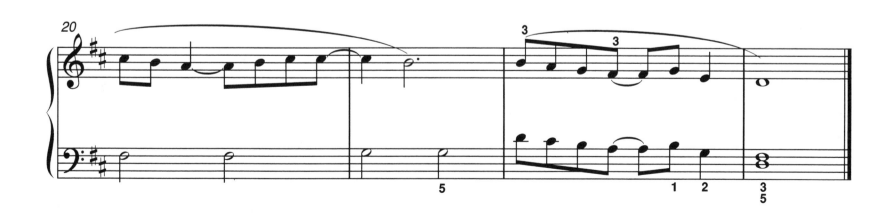

TELL ME IT'S NOT TRUE

by Willy Russell

Don't be tempted to rush bar eight when the time signature returns to $\frac{4}{4}$. Count very carefully.

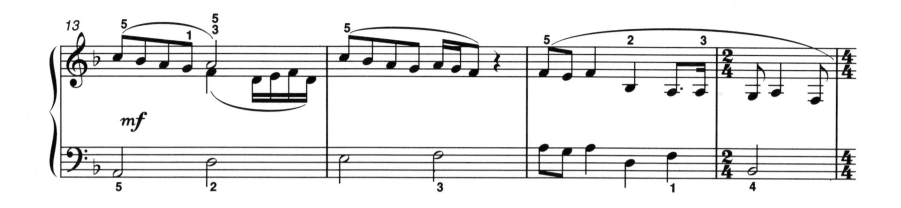

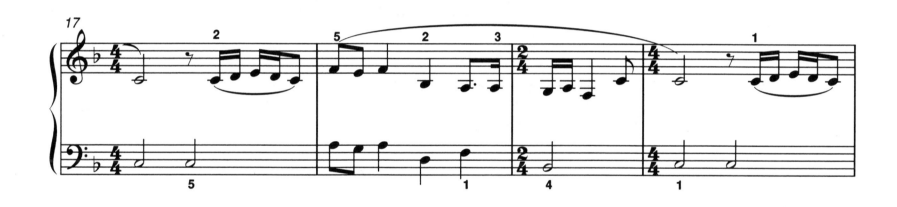

STREETS OF LONDON

by Ralph McTell

This song is usually sung with guitar accompaniment. Keep the left hand as light as possible when you play.

27

HEARTBEAT

by Bob Montgomery & Norman Petty

This tune from the popular television series 'Heartbeat' was originally sung by Buddy Holly.

LADY MADONNA

by John Lennon & Paul McCartney

Practise the left hand carefully before you try hands together.

This time the left hand should be played very firmly, to sound like a bass guitar.

31

THEME FROM 'ET (THE EXTRA-TERRESTRIAL)'

by John Williams

There are many accidentals in this piece. Make sure you read them very carefully.

6/01 (40662)